The Bird Table

Written by Pauline Cartwright • Illustrated by Cosmos Julien

Wintertime is cold.
There is snow on the hills.
It is hard for the birds to find food.
Dad and I made a bird table.
We put it up in the yard.

My sister and I put out food
for the birds.
We put seeds, suet,
and water on the table.

At first no birds came.

Then a brave sparrow
flew down.
He liked the food.
Peck, peck, peck.

Friends of the brave sparrow
watched him eat.
Then down they flew.
They liked the food, too.
Peck, peck, peck.

Other birds watched the sparrows.
Then down they flew.
They liked the food, too.
Peck, peck, peck.

Now, every day, birds feed at our table.
They squibble and squabble.
They flitter and flutter.
They peep and cheep.
And their beaks go peck, peck, peck.

Wintertime is cold.
There is snow on the hills.
It is hard for the birds to find food.
But there is plenty of food in *our* yard.

8